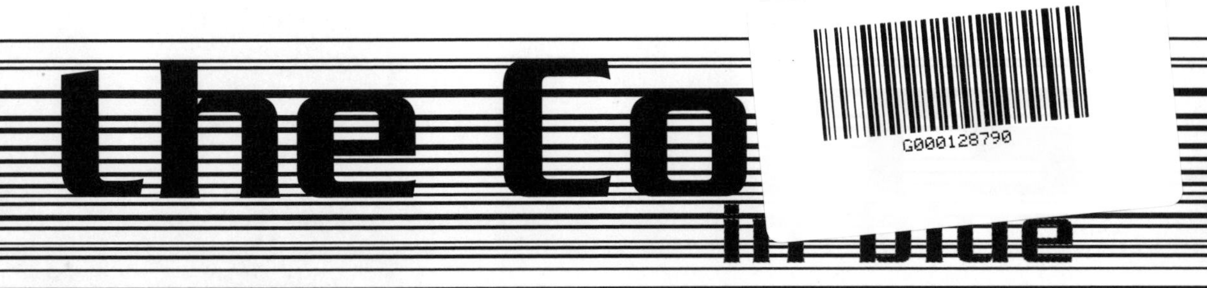

Wise Publications
London/New York/Sydney/Paris/Copenhagen/Madrid/Tokyo

Exclusive distributors:
Music Sales Limited
8/9 Frith Street, London W1D 3JB, England.
Music Sales Pty Limited
120 Rothschild Avenue, Rosebery, NSW 2018, Australia.

Order No.AM968198
ISBN 0-7119-8581-2

Music arranged by Derek Jones.
Music processed by Paul Ewers Music Design.

Printed in the United Kingdom by Caligraving Limited, Thetford, Norfolk.

Your Guarantee of Quality:
As publishers, we strive to produce every book
to the highest commercial standards.
The music has been freshly engraved and
the book has been carefully designed to
minimise awkward page turns and to make
playing from it a real pleasure.
Particular care has been given to specifying
acid-free, neutral-sized paper made from pulps which
have not been elemental chlorine bleached.
This pulp is from farmed sustainable forests and
was produced with special regard for the environment.
Throughout, the printing and binding have been
planned to ensure a sturdy, attractive publication
which should give years of enjoyment.
If your copy fails to meet our high standards,
please inform us and we will gladly replace it.

Breathless

Words & Music by R.J. Lange, Andrea Corr, Caroline Corr, Sharon Corr & Jim Corr

G♯m
F♯
B
F♯
1. The day - light's fad - ing slow - ly,
(Verse 2 see block lyric)
C♯m
G♯m
F♯
B
but time with you is stand - ing still. I'm wait - ing for
F♯
C♯m
G♯m
F♯
you on - ly, the slight - est touch and I feel weak.
E sus2
F♯
G♯m7
E sus2
F♯
I can - not lie, from you I can not hide.

B
E
F♯
And I'm los - ing the will to try.
D.%. (I've lost my)
G♯m7
fr4
E
F♯
Can't hide it, can't fight it. So
E
Aadd9
B
go on, go on, come on, leave me breath - less.
E
Aadd9
B
Tempt me, tease me un - til I can't de - ny this

E
Aadd9
B
To Coda
lov - ing feel - ing. Make me long for your kiss.
E
Aadd9
1.
B
N.C.
Go on, go on. Yeah, come on.
Drums
2.
B
N.C.
B
come on.
F♯
C♯m
fr4
Yeah, yeah.

G♯m
fr4
F♯
B
F♯
Ooh, yeah.
C♯m
fr4
G♯m
fr4
F♯
D.𝄋. al Coda
Yeah, yeah, yeah, yeah.
𝄌 Coda
N.C.
Aadd9
Go on, go on, come on,
B
E
Aadd9
leave me breath - less. Go on, go on, come on,

Verse 2:
And if there's no tomorrow
And all we have is here and now
I'm happy just to have you
You're all the love I need somehow
It's like a dream
Although I'm not asleep
And I never want to wake up
Don't lose it, don't leave it.

So go on, go on *etc.*

Give Me A Reason

Words & Music by Andrea Corr, Caroline Corr, Sharon Corr & Jim Corr

Em9
A9/E
fr2
Swim-ming, swim-ming in blue.
You left me lone - ly and con- fused.
Em9
A9
fr6
Em9
Ques-tion, ques-tion - ing you.
So soon good - bye,
A9/E
fr2
Em9
A9
fr6
you stole my heart.
I'm be-lieve, I'm be - liev - ing you.
(Verse 2 see block lyric)
Em9
A9/E
fr2
Em9
A9
fr6
Was it a lie right from the start?
An - swer, an-swer me do.

D
G
C
D
Well now my bo-dy's weak so just give me a rea - son. And my make-up's off
G
Am7
D
G
C
so just give me a rea - son. My de - fence is down so just give me a rea -
D
G
Am7
1.
Em9
- son. Give me a rea - son, give me a rea - son. 2. You will nev - er know.
2.
Em11
Violin
Am7
Em11
- son.

Am7
Em11
Am7
Em11
Am7
Em11
Am7
Em11
Am7
Em11
Am7
Em11

Am7
Em9
A9/E
So what's a girl like me to do?
Em9
A9
Em9
A9/E
Drown-ing, drown-ing in you.
And who's to save me from the blue,
Em9
A9
and car-ry, car-ry me through?
Perc.
D
G
C
D
Yes now my bo-dy's weak so just give me a rea - son. And my make-up's off

G Am7 D G C
so just give me a rea - son. My de - fence is down so just give me a rea -
D G Am7 D
- son. I am strong e - nough so give me a rea - son. My bo - dy is weak
G C D G Am7
so just give me a rea - son. And my make - up's off so just give me a rea -
D G C D
- son. My de - fence is down so just give me a rea - son. Give me a rea -

Verse 2:
You'll never know the love I felt
Wanting, waiting for you
It takes a weak heart to forget
Follow, follow it through.

Now my body's weak etc.

Somebody For Someone

Words & Music by Andrea Corr, Caroline Corr, Sharon Corr & Jim Corr

E♭
F
B♭
E♭
F
dead of the night. And her soul's in the su - gar and her heart's in her mind. And she's
B♭
E♭
F
cry-ing with a stran - ger for some - one to love. And she sings
F
E♭maj9
F
"Look at me, see me.
1° Tacet (Some-bo-dy's gon-na make it right. Some-bo-dy's gon-na make it right.
E♭maj9
F
Look at me, save me.
Some - bo - dy's gon-na make it right. Some-bo-dy's gon-na make it right.

E♭maj9
fr5
F
Free me,
find me cos if there's
Some-bo-dy's gon-na make it right.
Some-bo-dy's gon-na make it right.
E♭maj9
fr5
F
To Coda
some-bo - dy for some - one,
yeah look at me."
Some - bo - dy's gon-na make it right.)
(On D.%.) (Come)
1.
N.C.
B♭
Some-bo - dy for some - one.
2. There's a
Drums
2.
E♭
fr3
F
Violin

E♭
fr3
F
E♭
fr3
3
F
E♭/G
fr3
B♭sus4
B♭
3
F
B♭/F
F
(Some - bo - dy's gon - na make it right.
Some - bo - dy's gon - na make it right.
B♭/F
B♭sus4/F
F
D.%. al Coda
Some - bo - dy's gon - na make it right.
Some - bo - dy's gon - na make it right.)

Verse 2:
There's a deep boy at the corner shop
Watching sugar sell for money
To the dead at night
And he sees in her an angel
In the cruelest of worlds
Hiding in the darkness
Screaming out for love.

And he sings "Look at me" *etc.*

Say

Words & Music by Andrea Corr, Caroline Corr, Sharon Corr & Jim Corr

Dm7
Am
I can't see.
Gone are the days of precious love.
Re-lied on and leaned on.
D/F♯
Dm7/F
Am
So ma-ny days of sleep-less nights by your side.
D
Dm7
Am
And why, oh, why?
I nev-er thought that it would be like this.
D/F♯
F6
My first love, the last time.
But if he

C
G6/B
Am
D
say, say, says that he loves me, I can cry, I can smile.
F6
C
G6/B
Am
But if he say, say, says that he needs me, there's a light,
D
F
1.
Am7
there's a light, light for me.
D7sus4
Yeah, yeah, yeah, yeah.

Am7
Dm9
fr3
Say.
2.
N.C.
(Nev - er wan - na feel that a - gain, that a - gain. Nev - er
wan - na feel that a - gain.)
Am7
D/A
Con pedale
Am7
D/A
Am7

Am7
D/A
Am7
D/A
Am7
Repeat ad lib.
Lean on, got-ta re-ly on. Don't leave me. Don't leave me.
D/A
Am7
D/A
Lean on, got-ta re-ly on. Don't leave me. Don't
Gone are the days when I was young and free.
Am7
D/A
Am7
leave me. Lean on, got-ta re-ly on. Don't
Gone are the days of pre-cious love. Re-lied
D
F6
leave me. Don't leave me. But if he
on, and leaned on.

C
G6/B
Am
D
say, say, says that he loves me, I can cry, I can smile.
F6
C
G6/B
Am
But if he say, say, says that he needs me, there's a light,
D
1.
F6
2.
F6
there's a light. Yeah, if he Light for me.
Am7
D7sus4
Yeah, yeah, yeah, yeah.

Am7
Light for me.
(Say
Dm9
fr3
)
Am7
So many things that I
like to say but he took you-a-way,
D7sus4
took you a-way.
Am7
So ma-ny things I would like to ask.
Dm9
fr3
He took you a-way,

Verse 2:
So many things that I would like to say
But he took you, took you away
So many things I'd like to ask
It's no good, cos you're not here
I hear a voice, I see you laugh
And if only you were here
You see the night and I the day
But sometime we will walk away.

But if he say, say, say *etc.*

All The Love In The World

Words & Music by R.J. Lange, Andrea Corr, Caroline Corr, Sharon Corr & Jim Corr

Dadd9
E
A
Bm7add11
Dadd9
E
more than O. K.
I've got more than a girl could wish for.
A
Bm7add11
Dadd9
A
F
G
C
I live my dreams but it's not all they say.
Still I be - lieve
Dm7
F
G
C
Dm7
I'm miss - ing some - thing real.
I
F
G
need some - one who real - ly sees me.

D
Em7
G
Don't wan-na wake up a-lone a-ny-more,
still be-liev-ing you'll walk
D
E♭dim
Em
through my door.
All I need is to know it's for sure
then
Gm
fr3
1.
D
Em7
I'll give
all the love in the world.
D/F♯
G
A5
2.
D
Em9
3
Guitar

D/F♯
G6
D
Em9
D/F♯
G6
D
Em9
D/F♯
G6
D
Em9
D/F♯
Asus4
Em7
G
Asus4
Love's for a life-time not for a mo-ment, so how could I throw it a - way?
A
Em7
G
Yeah. I'm on - ly hu - man and nights grow cold - er with

Asus4
A
G
no-one to love me that way. Yeah. I need some-one who real-
A
E
F♯m7
-ly sees me. And I won't wake up a-lone a-ny-more
A
E
Fdim
still be-liev-ing you'll walk through my door. You'll reach for me and I'll know
F♯m
Am
it's for sure that I'll give all the love in the world.

Verse 2:
I've often wondered if love's an illusion
Just to get you through the loneliest days
I can't criticize it, I have no hesitation
My imagination just stole me away
Still I believe I'm missing something real
I need someone who really sees me.

Don't wanna wake up alone *etc.*

Radio

Words & Music by Andrea Corr, Caroline Corr, Sharon Corr & Jim Corr

A6/B
Eadd9/B
couples standing on the street sharin' Summer kisses and silly sounds.
Bsus2
Bm7
A6/B
Eadd9/B
Bsus2
Bm7
So I step inside, pour a glass of wine. With a
A6/B
Eadd9/B
Bsus2
full glass and an empty heart I search for something to occupy my mind.

Bm7
A6/B
E
F♯
Cos you
Dmaj7
F♯
Dmaj7
F♯
are in my head,
swim - ming for-ev-er in my head.
Tan-
Dmaj7
F♯
Dmaj9
fr4
- gled in my dreams,
swim - ming for - ev - er.
E
A6
C♯m7
fr4
So I lis - ten to the ra - di - o,
and all the songs we

Bsus4
B
E
A6
used to know.
So I lis - ten to the ra - di - o,
C♯m7
fr4
Bsus4
B
1.
Bsus2
re - mem - ber where we used to go.
Bm7
A6/B
E add9/B
2. Now it's
2.
E
A6
C♯m7
fr4
So I lis - ten to the ra - di - o,
and all the songs we

Bsus4
B
E
A6
used to know.
So I lis - ten to the ra - di - o,
C♯m7
fr4
Bsus4
B
Bsus2
re - mem - ber where we used to go.
Bm7
A6/B
Eadd9/B
F♯
Violin
3
You
Dmaj7
F♯
Dmaj7
are in my head, swim - ming for - ev - er.

Verse 2:
Now it's morning light and it's cold outside
Caught up in a distant dream
I turn and think that you are by my side
So I leave my bed and I try to dress
Wondering why my mind plays tricks
And fools me into thinking you are there
But you're still in my head
Swimming forever in my head
Not lying in my bed
Just swimming forever.

So listen to the radio *etc.*

Irresistible

Words & Music by R.J. Lange, Andrea Corr, Caroline Corr, Sharon Corr & Jim Corr

F♯m
D6
F♯m
(Ah.)
(Ah.
D
F♯m
D
) 1. Don't want you for the week - end. Don't want you for a day.
(Verse 2 see block lyric)
F♯m
D
F♯m
Don't need a love di - vi - ded. Don't
D
F♯m
Gmaj7
wan - na feel this way.
See I want you to need

A7
Gmaj7
me.
(The way I need you.)
Just like I need
A7
Gmaj7
you.
(The way I see you.)
And I want you to see
A7
Bm7
Gadd9
fr3
Bm7
A
me like no - one be - fore.
F
Gm7
fr3
B♭sus2
You're ir - re - sis - ti - ble. You're na - tu - ral, phy-

C
F
Gm7
fr3
- si - cal.
It's in - de - fi - na - ble.
You're ma -
B♭sus2
C
F
- gi - cal,
il - lo - gi - cal,
yeah.
So make-you - mine-
Gm7
fr3
B♭sus2
1.
Dm7
- a - ble.
You're mine.
F♯m
2.
Dm7
F♯m
D

F♯m7
Dadd9
fr2
Guitar
Gmaj7
A7
Now you feel what I'm feel - ing.
(Don't you feel what I'm feel - ing.)
Don't you know that it's more?

A7
Gmaj7
A7
It can take you to pla - ces like
(It can take you pla - ces.)
Bm7
Gadd9
fr3
Bm7
A
nev - er be - fore.
F
Gm7
fr3
B♭sus2
You're ir - re - sis - ti - ble. You're na - tu - ral, phy-
- ti - ble.)
C
F
Gm7
fr3
- si - cal. It's in - de - fi - na - ble. You're ma-

Verse 2:
So can't you see I'm tortured
Oh can't you hear my pain
If you just let me show you
I'll be your summer rain
Then you'll feel that you want me
(The way I'm feeling)
Just like I want you
(The way I want you)
And you'll know nothing's better
It's like nothing before.

You're irresistible *etc.*

One Night

Words & Music by Andrea Corr, Caroline Corr, Sharon Corr & Jim Corr

C/E
F
Em
G
My
heart aches
with a hun-
C/E
Dm7
G
G/F
- ger
and the
want that you were mine.
No, I can - not de-
C/E
F
Em
Am/E
Em
Am/E
- ny.
So for one
night
is it
al - right
that I
Dm7
G7sus4
G7
give
you
my heart,

C
C/E
Dm7
G7sus4
G7
my love, my heart, just for one night.
C
C/E
Dm7
G7sus4
G7
My body, my soul, just for one night.
C
C/E
Dm7
G7sus4
G7
To Coda
My love, my love for one night.
1.
C
C/E
Dm7
G
G7
One night, one night.

2.
Dm7
G6/9
G
Em
G/D
G
C
Dm
Dm7
Guitar
night.
G
G/F
C/E
F
For
Em
Am/E
Em
Am/E
one night it was so right that I
Dm7
G7sus4
G7
D.%. al Coda
gave you. My heart

Verse 2:
When morning awakes me
Well I know I'll be alone
And I feel I'll be fine
So don't you worry about me
I'm not empty on my own
For inside I'm alive.

That for one night
It was so right
That I gave you my heart, my love
My heart, just for one night
My body, my soul, just for one night
My love, I loved for one night
One night, one night.

All In A Day

Words & Music by Andrea Corr, Caroline Corr, Sharon Corr & Jim Corr

Cm7
F
E♭add9/G
F
Cm7
F
lie.
To her dis - may
E♭
F
Cm7
F
she saw the child that was in her
die.
1° only
E♭add9/G
F
Cm7
F
E♭maj7
F
And she cried
ov - er -
Cm7
F
E♭add9/G
F
Cm7
F
- night,
cos what she sees

E♭maj7
F
Cm7
F
E♭add9/G
F
she does - n't like.
Fm
A♭
B♭
Fm
A♭/E♭
I'm twist - ing. (Twist - ing.)
I'm turn - ing
B♭
E♭
B♭
Fm
A♭
B♭
(Turn - ing.) I'm ach - ing. (Ach - ing.)
Fm
A♭
B♭
Gm
Cm7
F
And it's burn - ing in one day,

1.
E♭sus2
F
Cm7
fr3
F
E♭add9/G
fr3
F
Violin
in one day.
2.
Cm7
fr3
F
E♭add9/G
fr3
F
Violin
In one day.
Cm7
fr3
F
E♭sus2
F
Cm7
fr3
F
E♭add9/G
fr3
F

Verse 2:
Just let me flow
Just let me drift on by
No more, no pain
I don't have tears to cry.

I'm twisting *etc.*

No More Cry

Words & Music by Andrea Corr, Caroline Corr, Sharon Corr & Jim Corr

Gm7
fr3
B♭6
shook me up, turned me 'round and made me cry till I would drown.
F5
B♭sus2
Stole the day - light, brought the night, so much an - ger I would fight.
Gm7
fr3
B♭6
Lost my youth a - mid the blue, saw all the lone - li - ness in you.
F5
B♭sus2
2. Wan - na help you, give you love, shine some light out from the mud.
(Verse 3 see block lyric)

Gm7
fr3
B♭6
Fill the emp - ty, find a rhyme, a bright-er day, a bet-ter time.
F5
B♭sus2
But I'm won - d'ring where I'm gone, can't find the truth with-in my song.
Gm7
fr3
B♭6
All I have I'll give to you, to let you know you're not a - lone.
C5
fr3
C
F
C
I'm tell - ing you: I'm

F
B♭sus2
Csus4
smil-ing for you on - - - ly. I'm try-ing for you sole-
C
- - ly. I'm pray-ing for you on - - - ly. No more cry,
1.
B♭6/9
no more cry.
2, 3.
no more cry.
I'm sing-ing for you on - - - ly. Hey, I

To Coda
F
B♭sus2
Csus4
C
F
B♭sus2
Csus4
wor - ry for you on - - ly. I'm pray - ing for you on -
F
B♭6/9
- - ly. No more cry, no more cry.
C5
B♭5
E♭
fr3
Reach out for your love. Shout out for your love.
Lis - ten for your love.

C5
B♭5
E♭
C
Be - lieve in her love.
N.C.
D.𝄋. al Coda
I'm tell - ing you, I'm tell - ing you: I'm
⊕ Coda
C
F
B♭sus2
Csus4
- ly. But it's you saves me from lone - - - ly. No more cry,
F
B♭sus4
Csus4
C
F
B♭sus2
Csus4
no more cry. No, no more cry.
(No more cry.

Verse 2:
I wanna hear you laugh again
Without the ache to bring you down
No, we'll never be the same
If only I could take your pain
If it's true what people say
There still is beauty in each day
We'll find comfort in her strength
And one day soon we'll meet again
I'm telling you:

I'm smiling for you *etc.*

At Your Side

Words & Music by Andrea Corr, Caroline Corr, Sharon Corr & Jim Corr

Em7
and you need a friend just to be a - round,
A7sus4
A7
D
I will com - fort you,
G6
I will take your hand and I'll pull you
Cadd9
Cmaj9
A7sus4
A7
through, I will un - der - stand. And you'll know that

Dsus2
G6
Em7
I'll be at your side.
There's no need
A7sus4
Dsus2
G6
to worry. To-ge-ther we'll sur-vive
Em7
A7sus4
Dsus2
through the haste and hur-ry.
I'll be at
G6
Em7
A7sus4
your side
when you feel like your a-lone
(if)

1.
Cadd9
To Coda
A7sus4
A7
or you've no - where to turn.
(and)
Dsus2
G6
Violin
I'll be at your side.
Em7
A7sus4
Dsus2
G6
Em7
A7sus4
2. If life's stand - ing

2.
A
Gmaj7
turn. (Side.)
I'll be at your
A
Gmaj7
side.
(I'll be, I'll be at your side.)
A
Gsus2
I'll be at your side.
(I'll be, I'll be at your side.)
A
G/A
fr3
Em/A
D.%. al Coda
I'll be at your side.

Verse 2:
If life's standing still
And your soul's confused
And you cannot find
What road to choose
If you make mistakes
You won't let me down
I will still believe
I won't turn around.

And you know that I'll be at your side *etc.*

Rain

Words & Music by Andrea Corr, Caroline Corr, Sharon Corr & Jim Corr

Gm7add11
C/G
Gm7add11
Fall - en an - gel
C7sus4
C7
Cm7
spin-ning from the light. And slip-ping, slid - ing in - to heav-en - ly lace.
Gm7add11
C/G
Cm7
But it's all, it's al - right
Gm9
Cm7
Gm9
now, cos we're liv-ing for this night for so long now. Yes it's all,

Cm7
fr3
E♭maj7
F6
it's al - right.
We are liv - ing on
Gm7add11
C7sus4
fr3
C7
hope,
we are liv - ing on
life.
De - pend - ing on
Cm7
fr3
F11
Gm7add11
3
truth
un - til the day we
die.
We are liv - ing on
C7sus4
fr3
C7
hope,
we are liv - ing on
life.
De - pend - ing on

1.
Cm7
F11
Gm7add11
C/E
B♭/F
C/G
truth until the day we die.
2.
Gm7add11
C9
Gm7
Dm9sus4
die.
Violin
E♭maj7
Dm7
Cm7
But it's all, it's al - right
Gm9
Cm7
now, cos we're liv - ing for this night for so long

Gm9
fr3
Cm7
fr3
now. Yes it's all, it's al - right.
E♭maj7
F6
We are liv - ing on
Gm7add11
C7sus4
fr3
C7
hope, we are liv-ing on life. De-pend-ing on
Cm7
fr3
F11
Gm7add11
3
truth un - til the day we die. We are liv-ing on

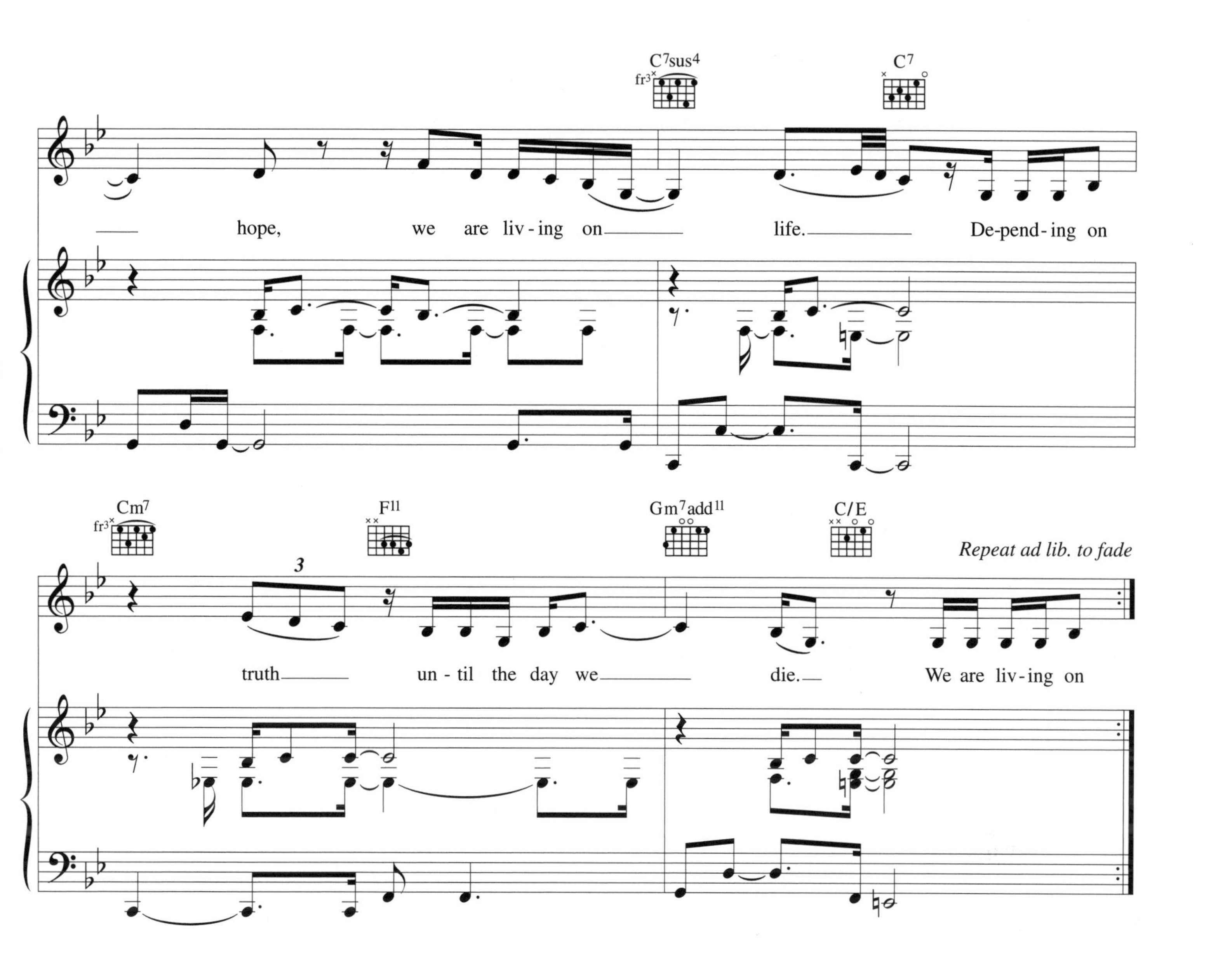

Verse 2:
Lost and lazy, floating through the dawn
And twisting, turning in a hazy mist
Guardian angel of silver and ice
Sleeping, sinking in a stream of light
But it's all, it's alright now
Cos we're living for this night for so long now
Yes it's all, it's alright.

We are living on hope *etc.*

Give It All Up

Words & Music by Andrea Corr, Caroline Corr, Sharon Corr & Jim Corr

Gm7
fr3
B♭
C
hap - pi - est
just when I'm with you.
Dm
Gm7
2. There's a dis - tance be - tween us
(Verse 3 see block lyric)
B♭
C
Dm
so far that I can't reach.
The stage lights, they
Gm7
B♭
C
shine so bright - ly,
but still I find no peace.
And I'm a

Gm7
fr3
C
F
C
long, long— way from— you.—
I'd give it all up just for you,—
Gm7
fr3
B♭
F
C
— just to have— you near me.
I'd give it all up just for you.—
Gm7
fr3
B♭
F
C
Gm7
fr3
B♭
— You bring me up, you bring me down,— you turn me in - side out.—
1.
2.
F
C
Gm7
fr3
B♭
Gm7
fr3
I'd give it all up just for you.—
—

F
C
Gm7
fr3
B♭
I'd give it all up just for you, just to have you near me.
F
C
Gm7
B♭
F
C
I'd give it all up just for you.
You bring me up, you bring me down,
Gm7
B♭
F
C
Gm7
you turn me in - side out.
I'd give it all up just for you.
E♭m
B♭
Dm
3
Guitar
8vb
Strings

Am
E♭m
B♭
Guitar
8vb
Strings
3
Dm
Gm7
fr3
C
D
G
D
Am7
C
I'd give it all up just for you, just to have you near me.
G
D
Am7
C
I'd give it all up just for you.

Verse 3:
I've been hearing some stories
Of couples so in love
But they've spent so much time apart
That it never seems to work
And I'm a long, long way from you.

Still I'd, I'd give it all up *etc.*

Rebel Heart

Music by Andrea Corr, Caroline Corr, Sharon Corr & Jim Corr

D
E7
A
D
E7
A
G
A
G
A
1.
D
E
2.
D
E
A
D
E7
A
D
E7
A
D
E7
Repeat ad lib. to fade
A
G
A
G
A
D
E

Hurt Before

Words & Music by Andrea Corr, Caroline Corr, Sharon Corr & Jim Corr

Cadd9
D
G/B
But at night she's a - lone, she's dream-ing of some - bo - dy new.
Cadd9
D
Em
Her some - one for to hold. She's pray-ing the dream will come true.
Cmaj9
D
Em7
Cmaj9
Show me the way. Show me, show me how. Help me be brave
D
G/B
Cmaj9
D
Em7
for love. Show me the way. Show me, tell me

Cmaj9
D
how. What do you say?
Cadd9
D
2. There's a pain in her heart, she's try-ing so hard to un-wind.
Cadd9
D
Makes her cry in the night when vi-sions so real make her blind.
Cadd9
D
Wants to break through the fear, e - ras-ing the scars from with-in.

Cadd9
D
Start a new kind of being, she's down and she's pray - ing a - gain.
Cadd9
D
Show me the way.
Show me, show me
Cadd9
D
G/B
Cadd9
how. Help me be brave for love.
Show me the way.
D
Cadd9
D
G/B
Show me tell me how. What do you say?
You see she's

Cadd9
D
G/B
turn-ing the key, un-lock-ing the door, em-brac-ing the rol - ler coast - er world.
Cadd9
D
G
Step-ping out - side with bo - dy and soul, tak-ing what-ev - er fu - ture holds.
Cadd9
D
G/B
Turn-ing the key, un - lock-ing the door, em-brac-ing the rol - ler coast - er world.
Cadd9
D
To Coda
You take it in stride, you're just twen - ty five. You know we've all been hurt be - fore.

Em
D/F♯
Em/G
D
3
Violin
Cmaj7
D
Em
D/F♯
Em/G
D
Cmaj7
D
G/B
D.%. al Coda
You see she's

Coda
Cadd9
D
G/B
Yeah, we've all been hurt be - fore.
Cadd9
D
G
So you're not a - lone,
Cadd9
D
G/B
no.
You're not a - lone.
Cadd9